Stock and Rocket

Published in 2023
First published in the UK by Stock and Rocket
An imprint of Igloo Books Ltd
Cottage Farm, NN6 0BJ, UK
Owned by Bonnier Books
Sveavägen 56, Stockholm, Sweden
www.igloobooks.com

0223 005
4 6 8 10 9 7 5
ISBN 978-1-78905-287-9

© iStock / Getty Images

Written by Joff Brown
Illustrated by Gareth Conway

Printed and manufactured in China

This book belongs to:

....

The Big Day Out

Gordon the Brachiosaurus was the biggest, nicest dinosaur in town.
He would do anything for his friends. One day, Gordon and his buddies were
getting ready to visit Prehistoric Park, the most exciting theme park, ever.

"I've hurt my foot!" cried Gordon's friend, Summer.
"Oh, no, I'll never make it to the bus for Prehistoric Park."
"Get on my back," said Gordon, with a smile. "I'll carry you there."
Summer hopped on and before long they were at the bus stop.

"Hey, Gordon," said the bus driver. "A wheel on the bus is broken.
We won't get to Prehistoric Park unless we change it. Can you help?"
Gordon summoned all his strength and lifted the bus,
while the driver changed the wheel.

Gordon was about to get on the bus when he saw his
friend, Becky, crying. "My ball is stuck up a tree," she said.
Gordon reached up with his long neck and grabbed the ball for Becky.
"Come on, Gordon!" called his friends. "We're leaving for Prehistoric Park!"

Gordon ran to the bus. He pushed and squeezed and tried to get in, but the door was too small. Gordon couldn't fit.

"Goodbye," he said, walking away from the bus, sadly. "Have fun without me."

Later, Gordon was sitting miserably at home,
when he heard a BEEP-BEEP coming from outside.
It was the bus, with an enormous chair tied to the back of it.
"We made this for you," Gordon's friends said. "Hop aboard!"

Gordon jumped on and the bus sped to Prehistoric Park. When they got there, Gordon squeezed onto the roller coaster, taking up a whole carriage. "Woooo!" he cried, as the roller coaster zoomed around the track.

Gordon and his friends had an amazing day at Prehistoric Park.
"The rides were great, but the best one of all was the ride here
on the bus," said Gordon, "thanks to my brilliant friends."

Sean the Show-off

Sean the Spinosaurus was the biggest show-off in school.
"I'm the best at everything," Sean would say to his friends.
"Stop bragging all the time," his friends would reply.

One day, in gym class, the dinosaurs were training on a trampoline. "I'm the best at trampolining," said Sean. He bounced up really high on the trampoline. Boing, boing, boing! All his friends went flying off.

After, it was time for music class. "I'm the best at music," said Sean. When he blew into his trumpet, it was so loud, everybody dropped their instruments in surprise. "Stop being a show-off," his friends said.

On the basketball court, Sean grabbed the basketball every time.
"Pass it to us!" yelled his friends. Instead, Sean barged past
everyone and bounced the ball into the basket to score.

The next day, the teacher announced a special treat for the class. "It's time for a swimming lesson," he said. Everyone clapped and cheered, but Sean went very quiet. He didn't know how to swim.

Everyone jumped in the pool, while Sean stood on the side, shivering.
"I don't like it. I want to go home!" he cried. Sean's friends were amazed.
"We thought you were the best at everything!" they said.

"If I'm not the best, then nobody will like me!" Sean wailed.
"Don't be silly," his friends said. "We like you because of YOU,
even though you're a show-off. We'll help you to learn to swim."

At the next lesson, Sean's friends gave him a pair of armbands and goggles. Soon, Sean was splashing and sploshing around. "I may not be the best at everything," Sean said, "but I definitely do have the best friends, ever!"